ARMOR UP!

by Jordan Leonhardt

DORRANCE
PUBLISHING CO
EST. 1920
PITTSBURGH, PENNSYLVANIA 15238

Dorrance Publishing Co
585 Alpha Drive
Suite 103
Pittsburgh, PA 15238
Visit our website at www.dorrancebookstore.com

ISBN: 978-1-6366-1240-9
eISBN: 978-1-6366-1827-2

ARMOR UP!

As the sunlight begins to show through my window, I hear my mom singing down the hall, "Wake up, wake up I say. It's already a beautiful day!"

I rub my eyes, pull back the covers, and jump to my feet. "Today is going to be awesome!"

As I begin to get ready for a fun day at school, my mom says, "Remember to put on the full Armor of God!"

I jump up and down.
"Oh yeah! I love putting on my Armor."

Now, where is my...

I found it! The Belt of Truth... my very first piece to put on for the day. I must have the Belt of Truth because it helps me stand firm and upright all day long!

The Bible says God's truth is light. If I don't have God's truth, my day could get messy and dark. I can't forget to strap on my belt!

Next, I am putting on the Breastplate of Righteousness. I must have on my breastplate because it protects my heart and helps me live my life according to God's word.

The Bible says righteousness is right living and my heart is the source of my life...I definitely need The Breastplate of Righteousness so that I can protect my heart!

Now for the Shoes of Peace...I can't forget to wear the Shoes of Peace because they help me stand firm, too. When I do forget these shoes, it feels like I'm on shaky ground and that can be scary!

The Bible says that peace comes from the Good News and that Jesus is the Prince of Peace. So, when I wear my Shoes of Peace, I know Jesus is who I stand with!

Hmmmm... What's next? Oh yeah! The Shield of Faith! I must have the Shield of Faith because it keeps me safe and protected throughout the whole day. When life throws bad things my way, all I have do is sling my shield in front of me and I am protected!

The Bible says that the Shield of Faith shields me from the fiery arrows of the enemy. When I use my Shield of Faith, I protect myself so that I can always be who God made me to be.

The next piece of Armor is very important... the Helmet of Salvation! It is important for me to put on my helmet because it protects my mind against the enemy and reminds me that I am saved because of Jesus.

The Bible says that Jesus came to earth to save you and me. When I put on my Helmet of Salvation, I know that Jesus is with me all day long. He loves, protects, and fights for me.

Finally, my favorite piece of armor...
The Sword of the Spirit!

I love my sword because it is my weapon that God has given me. The Sword of the Spirit gives me confidence and helps me feel unafraid!

The Bible says that the Sword of the Spirit is the Word of God. That means when I take up my sword, I tell the whole world, "Jesus is with me!" And that is so much fun!

Now, I have on the full Armor of God. Nothing can stop me today!

Well, here we are! All ready for school! Me and my friends have on our armor. Don't we look cool?

Now, before we go, I have a message just for you...

It's a simple reminder of what Jesus says to do!

Be strong in The Lord and his mighty power, for every piece of armor is ours!

So, what are you waiting for? Now, it's your turn to get ready and ARMOR UP too!

CPSIA information can be obtained
at www.ICGtesting.com
Printed in the USA
LVHW071443030521
686341LV00013B/367